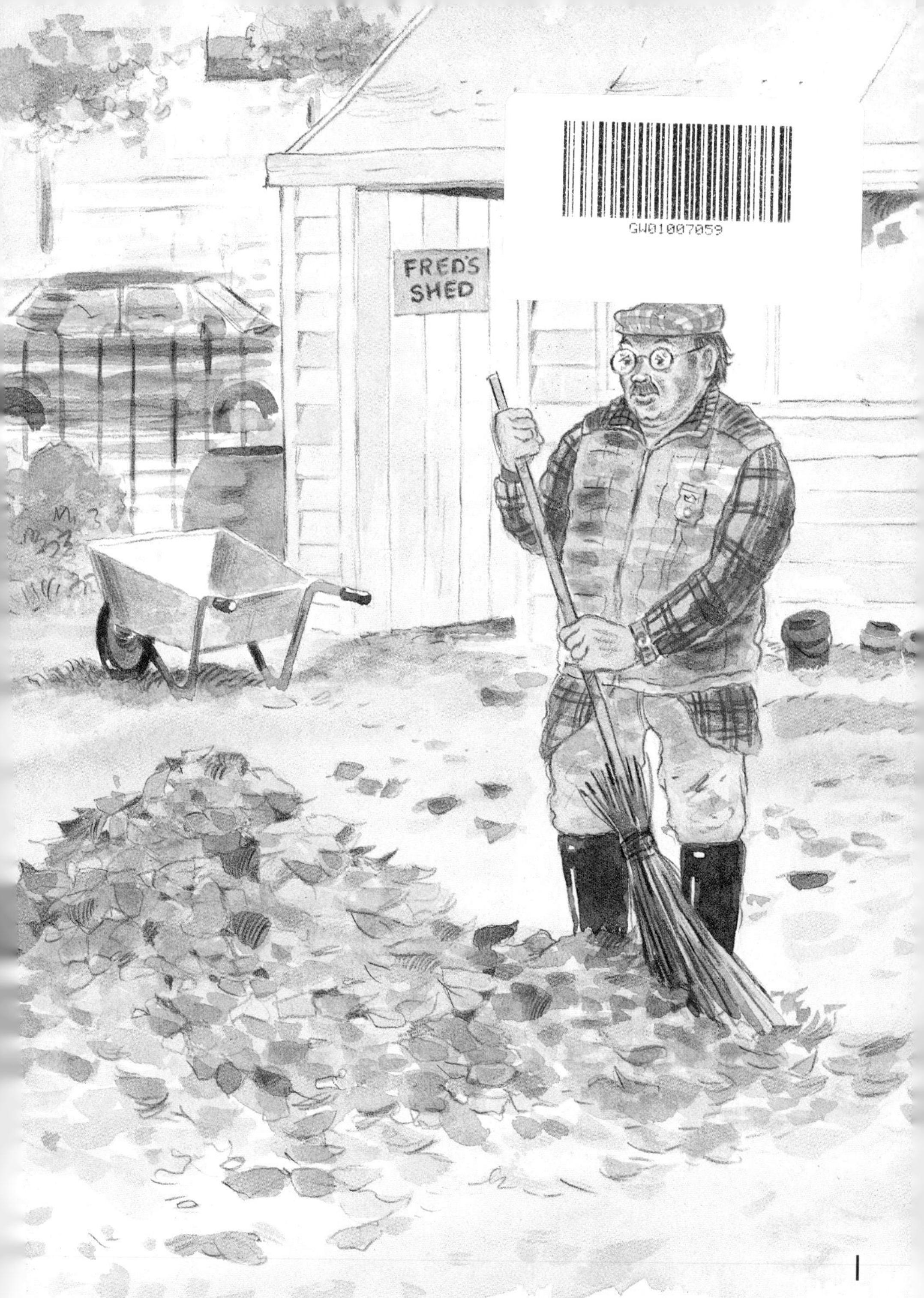
FRED'S
SHED

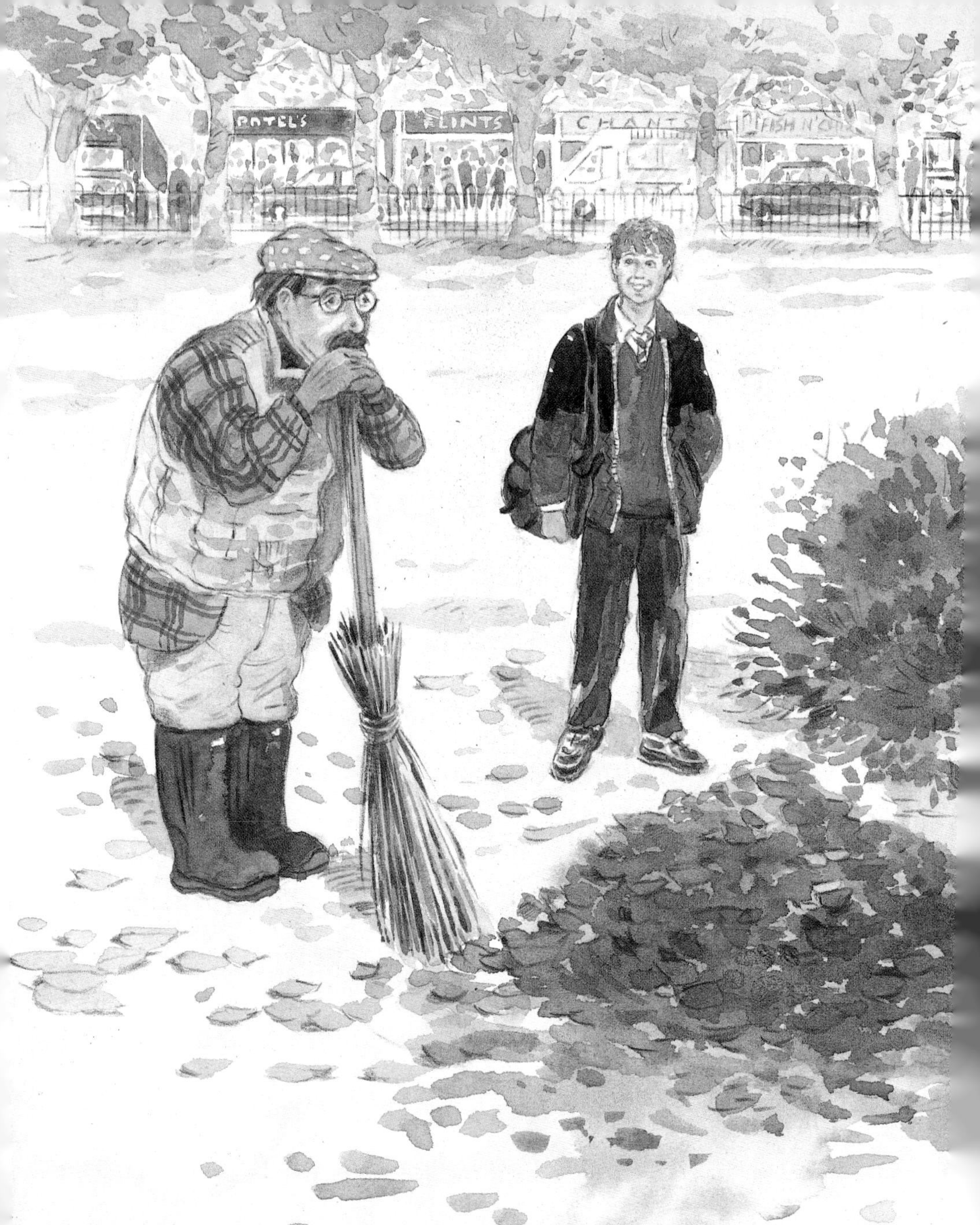
PATEL'S
FLINTS
CHANTS

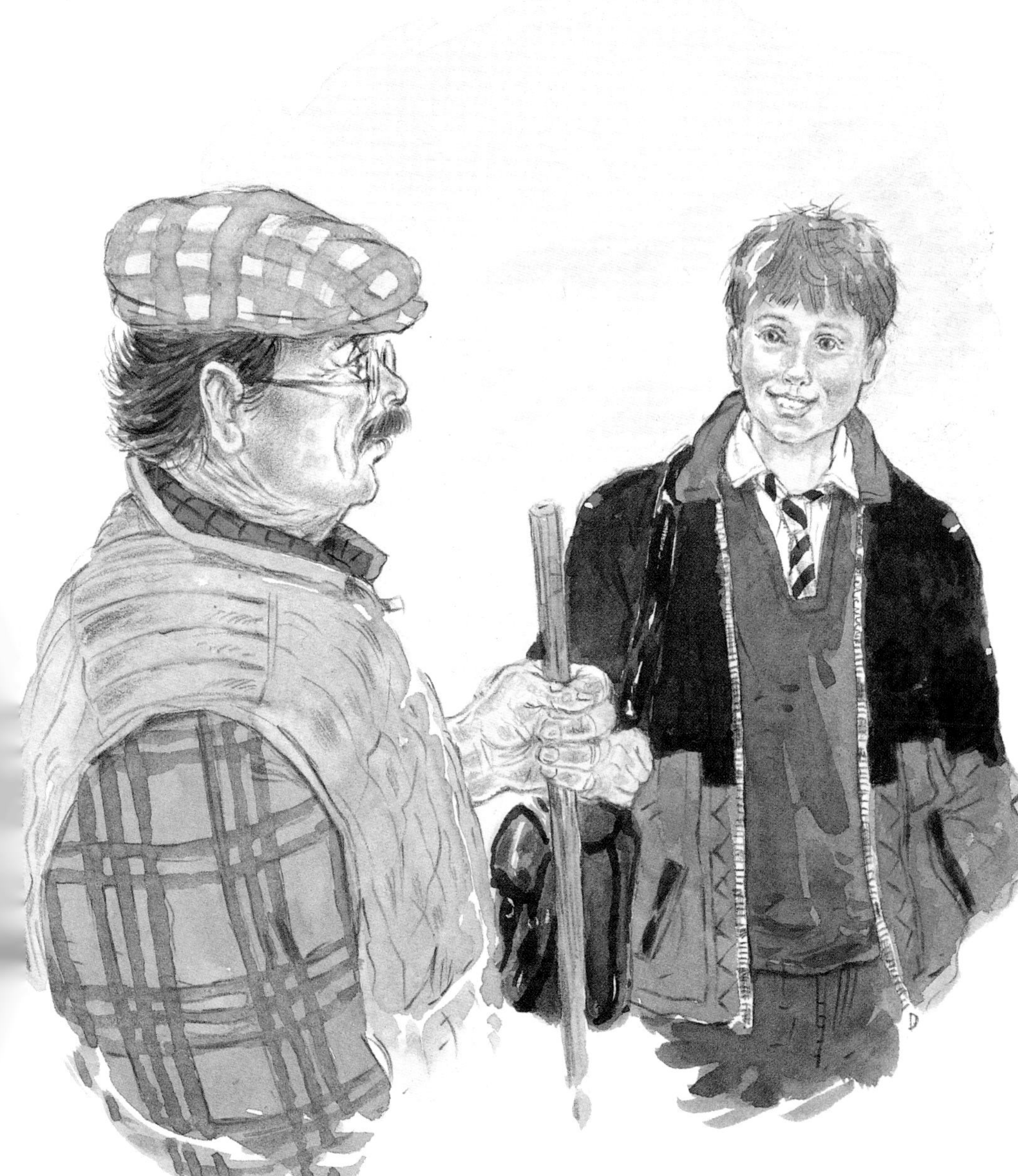

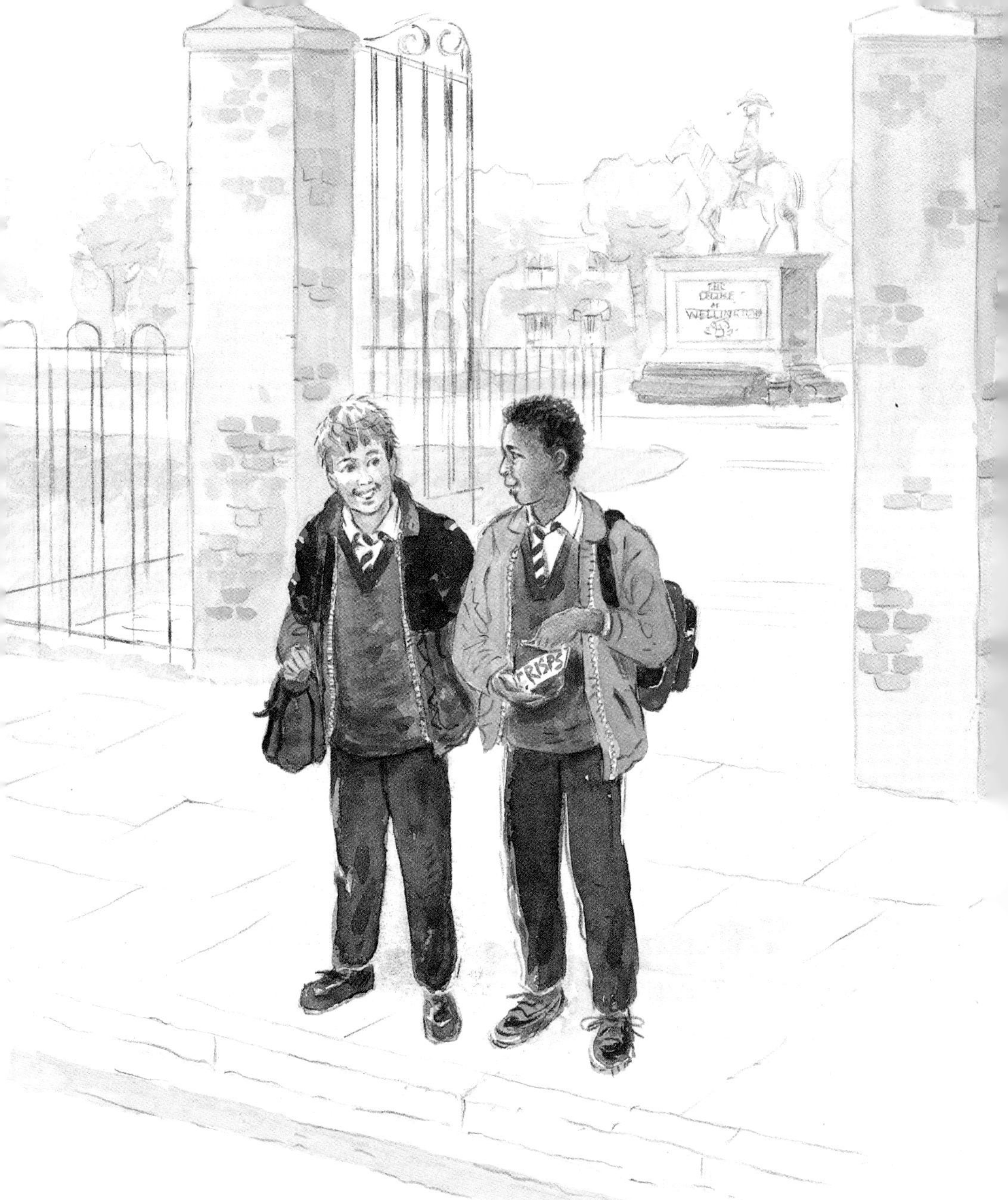
CRISPS

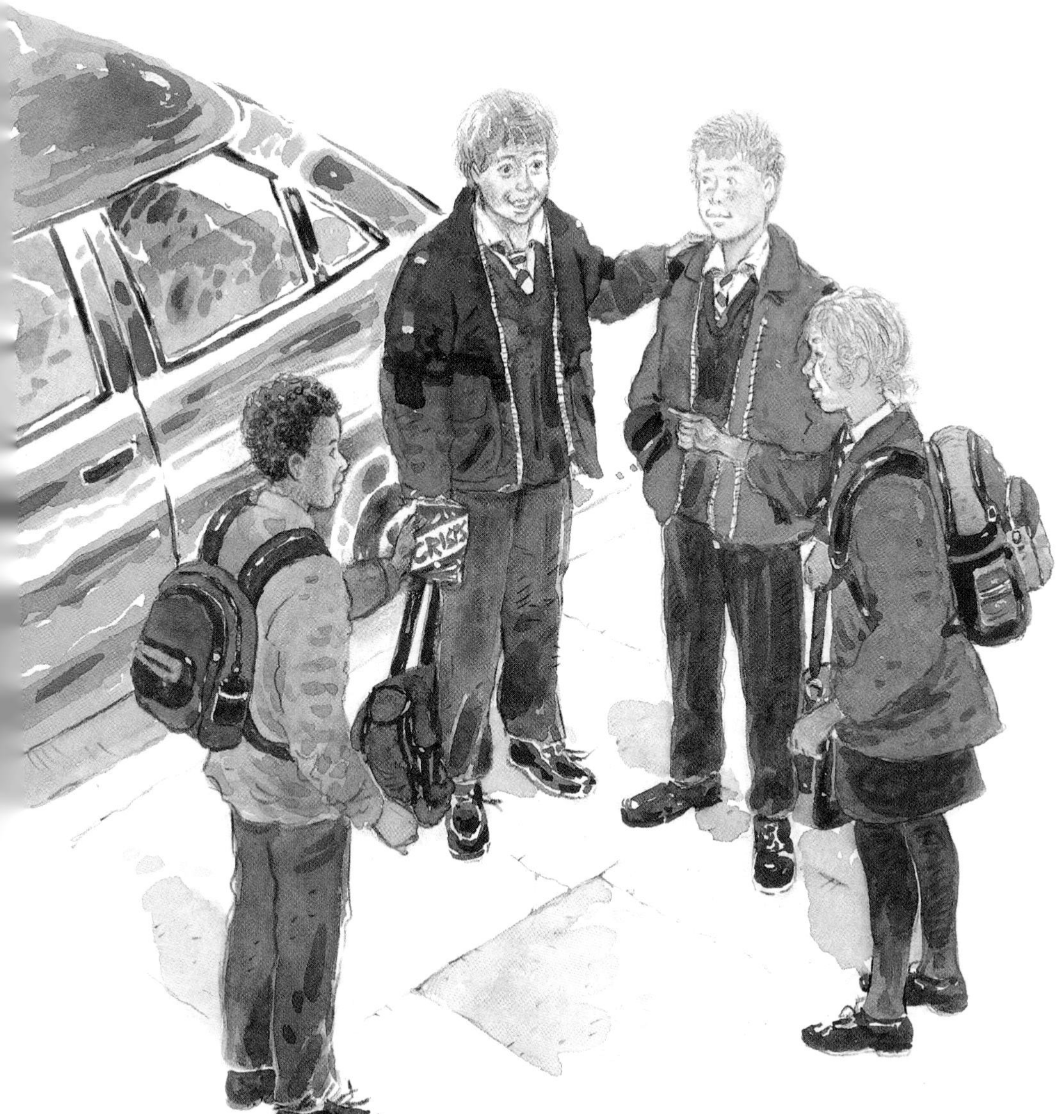
CRISPS

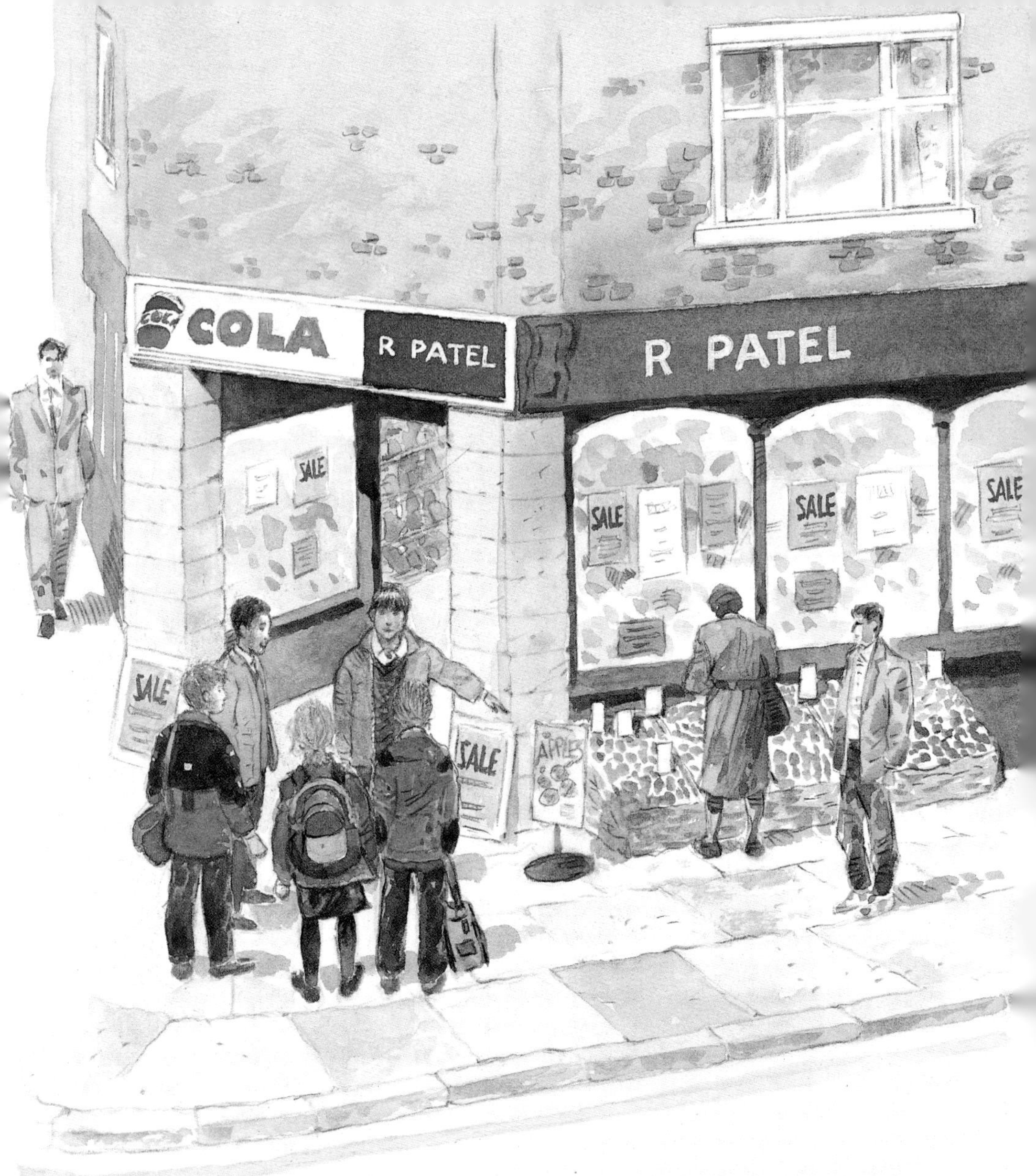
COLA
R PATEL
R PATEL
SALE
SALE
SALE
SALE
SALE
SALE
APPLES

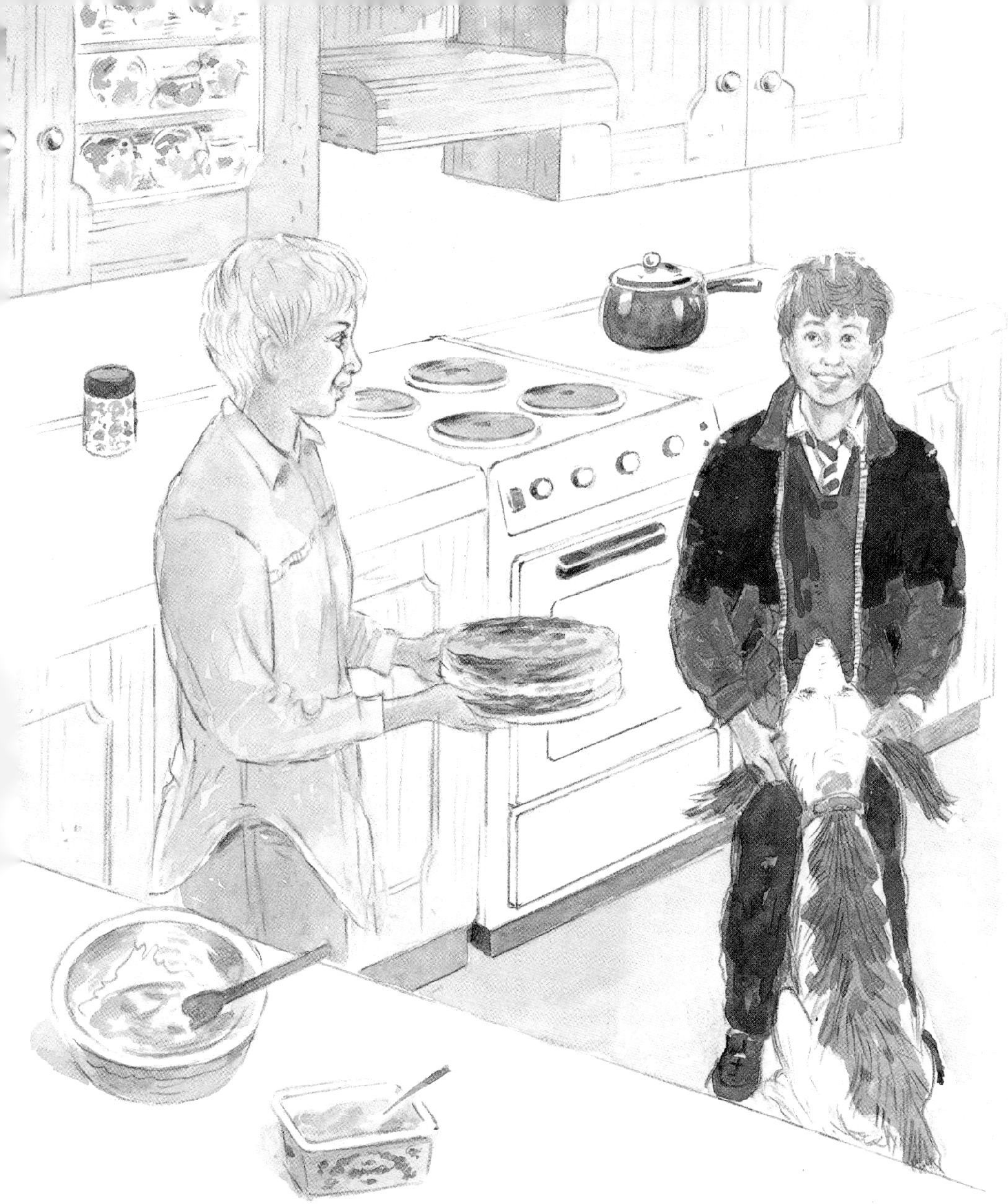

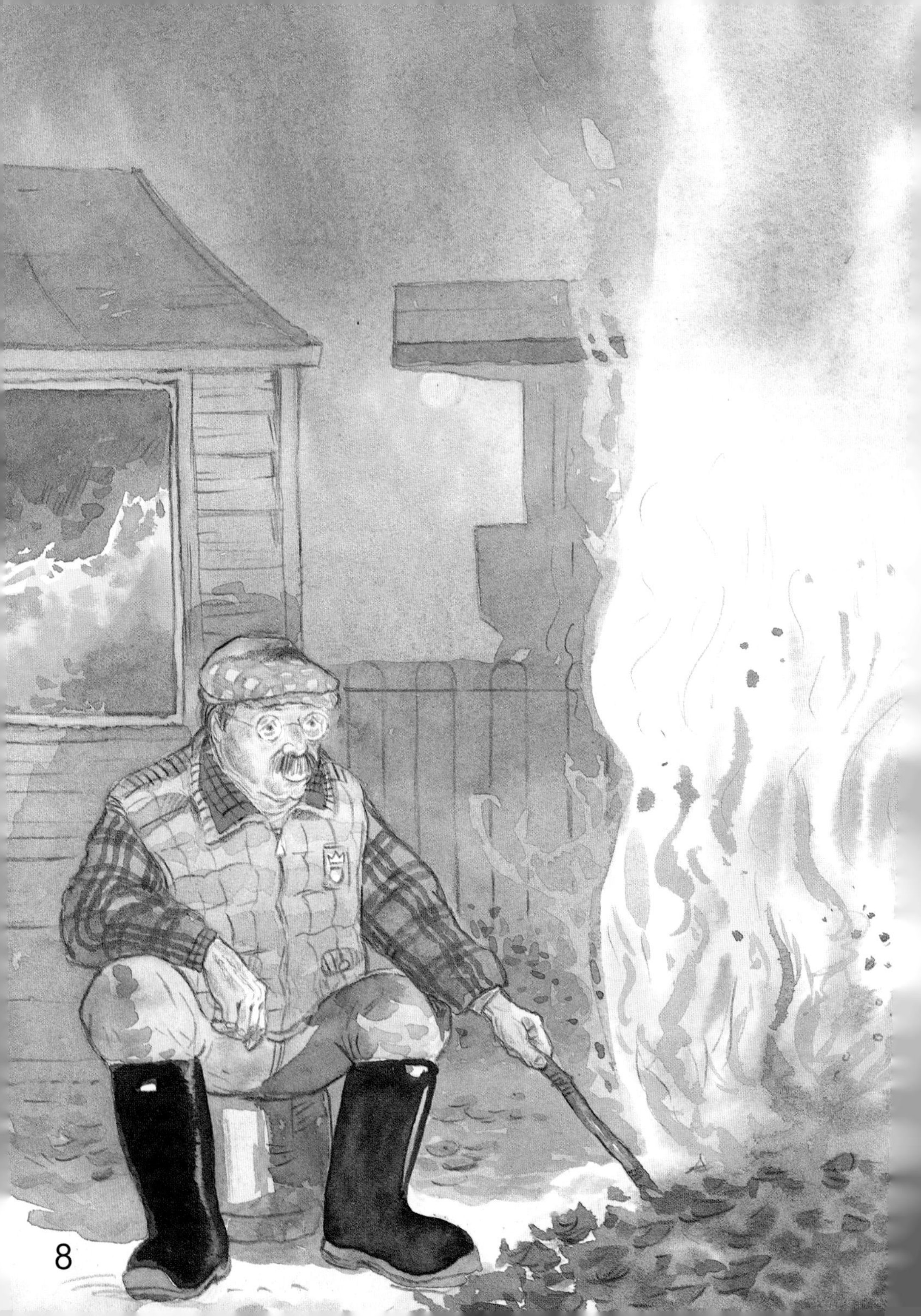

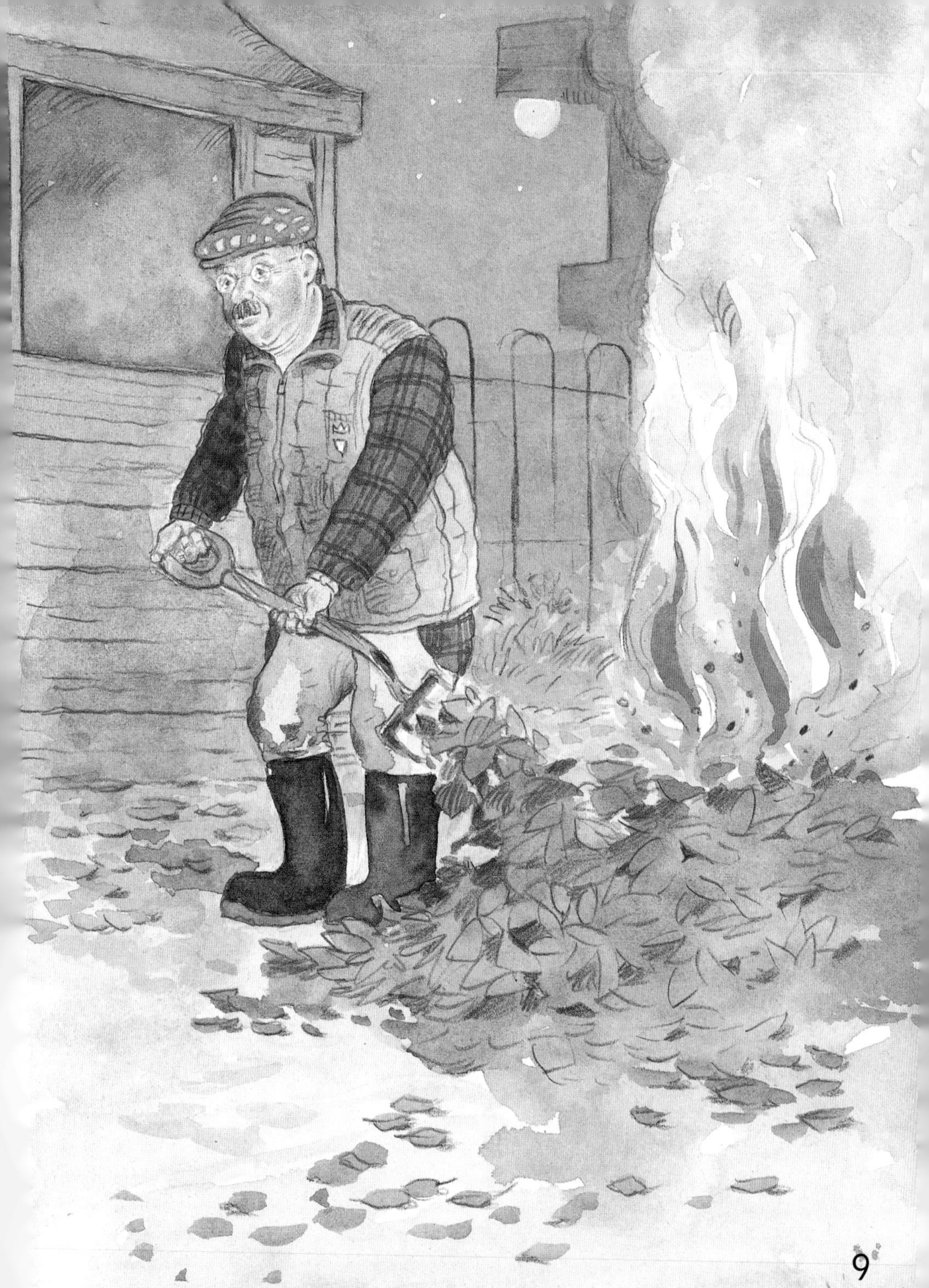

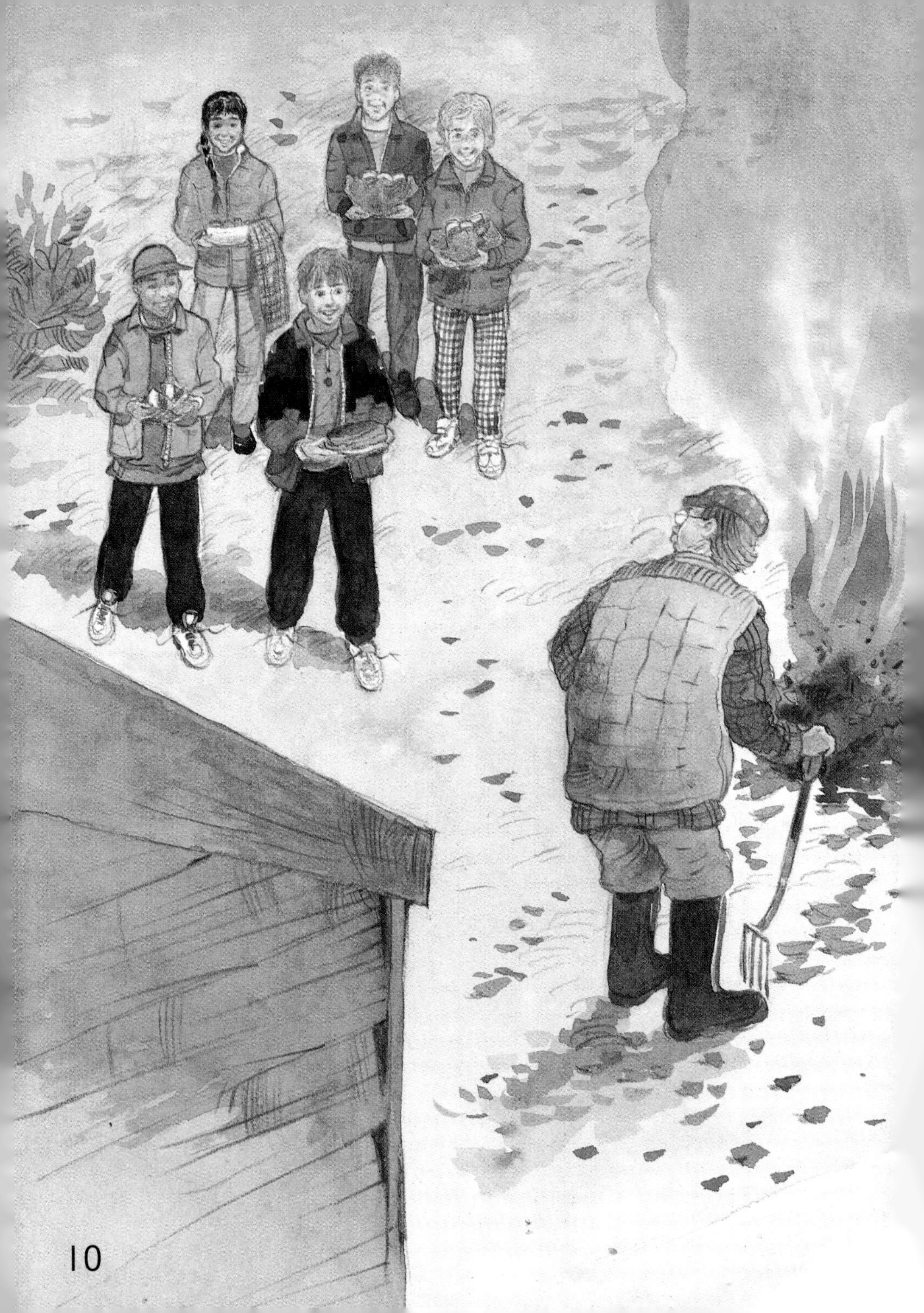

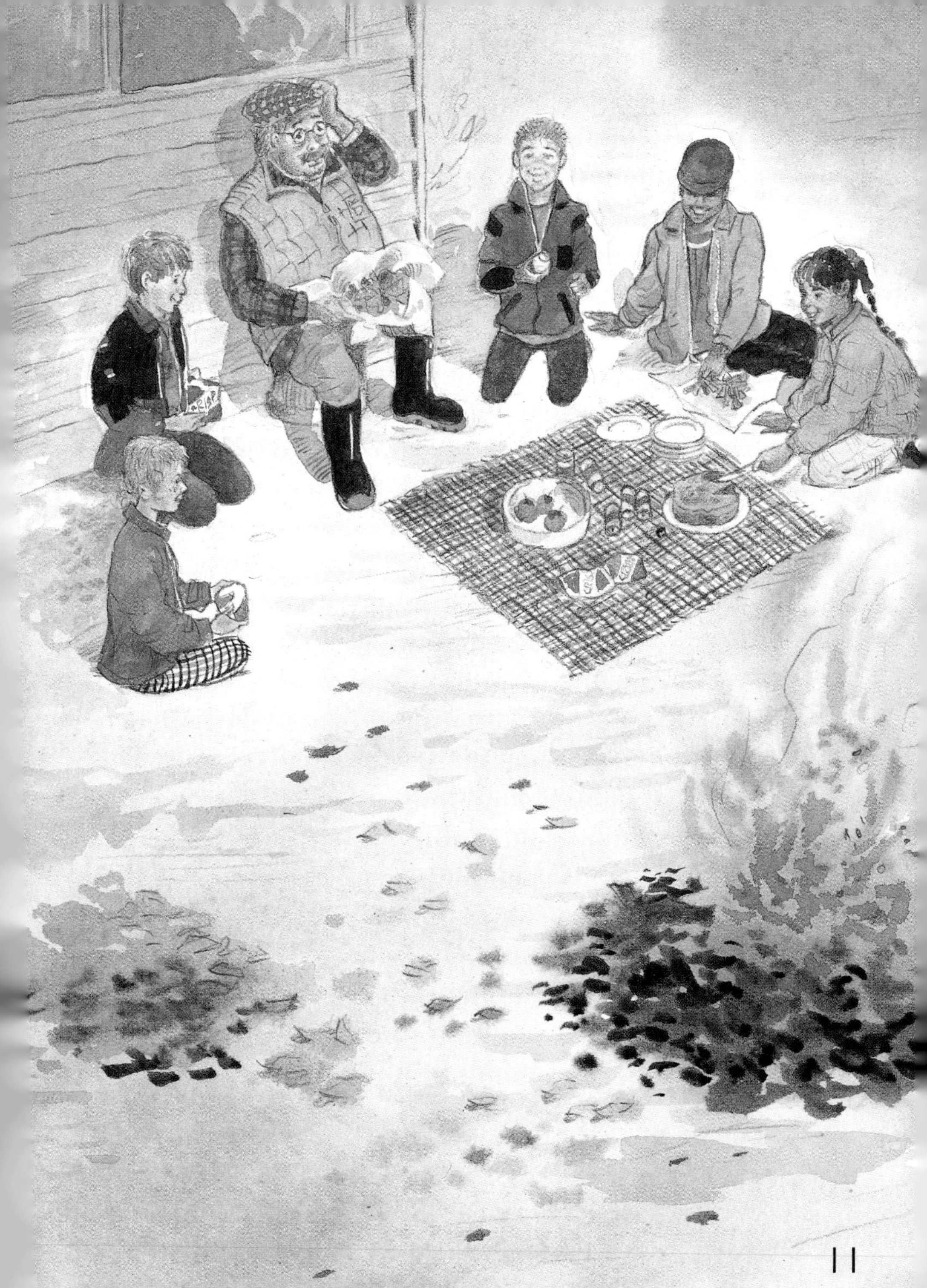

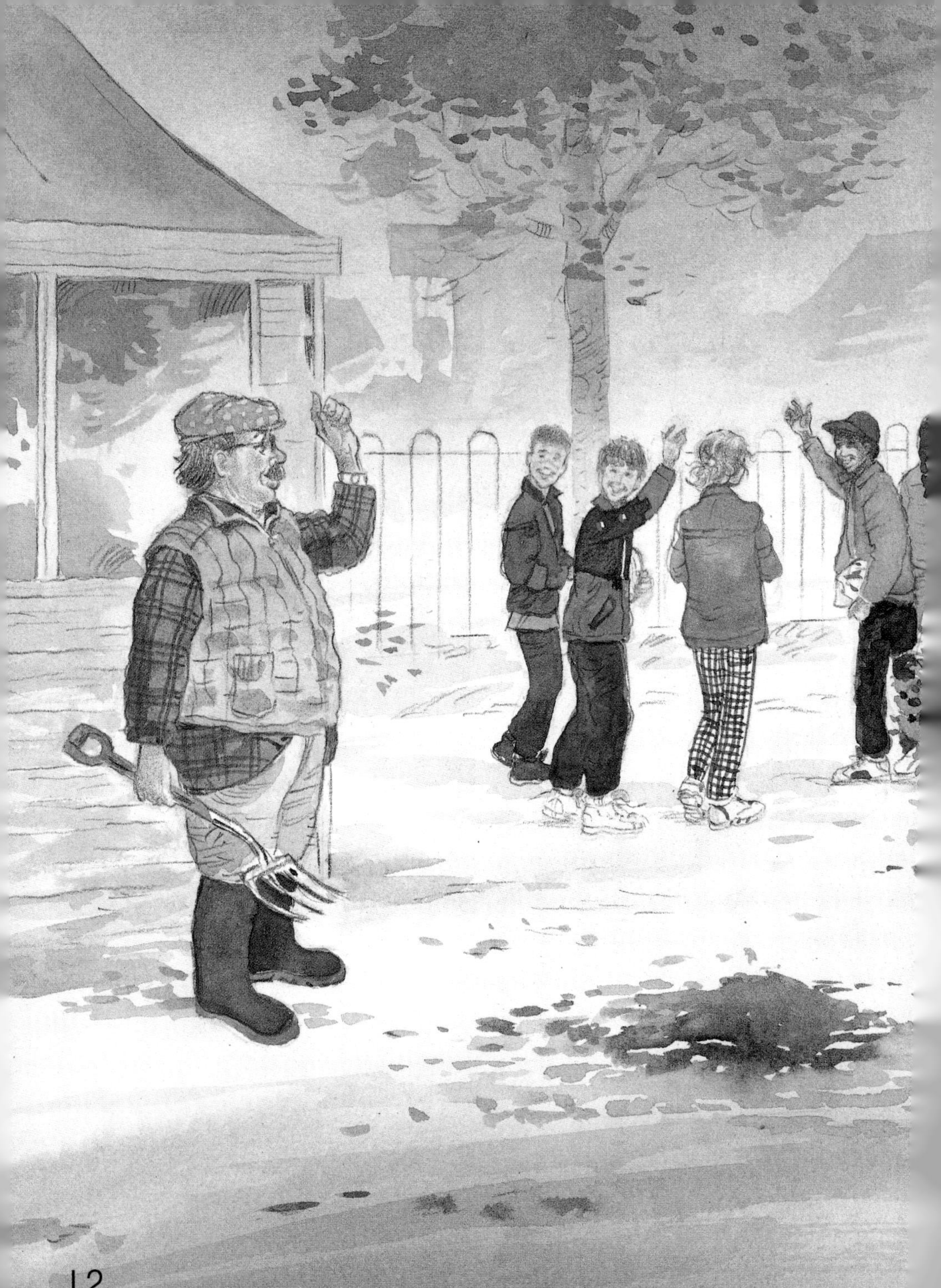